Fair's Fair

Written by Narinder Dhami

Illustrated by Philippe Dupasquier

Chapter 1

Lee had two best friends called
Raj and Sam. They all lived in the
same street, next door to each other.
One Saturday Raj went to see Sam.
"I've got some great news," said Raj.
"The fair has come to town and my
dad said he will take us tonight."
"Great!" said Sam.

Then Raj and Sam went to
Lee's house.
"We've got some great news,"
said Sam.
"The fair has come to town and
my dad said he will take us tonight,"
said Raj.
"Cool!" said Lee.

"We can go on the ghost train,"
said Raj.

"We can go on the big wheel,"
said Sam.

"And we can eat lots of candy floss,"
said Lee.

"YES!" said Raj, Sam and Lee.

Sam ran into her house.

Her dad was in the kitchen.

"Can I go to the fair tonight?" she asked. "Raj's dad said he will take us."

"OK," said Sam's dad. "But don't be back too late."

Lee ran into his house.

His mum was giving the baby a bath.

"Can I go to the fair tonight?"
he asked. "Raj's dad said he will
take us."

"I'm sorry, Lee," said his mum.

"I don't have any money for the
fair this week."

"But Raj and Sam are going,"
said Lee.

"I'm sorry, Lee, but you can't go," said
his mum.

Lee was fed up. He went back to his friends.

"I can't go to the fair," he said.

"Why not?" asked Sam.

"Because I haven't got any money," said Lee.

"You've got to come with us," said Raj. "Or it won't be any fun."

"But I haven't got any money," said Lee.

"We'll get some money for you,"
said Sam.

"How?" asked Lee.

"We can do some jobs for our mums
and dads," said Sam. "Then they
can pay us."

"What jobs can we do?" asked Lee.

"We can wash cars," said Sam.

"We can do the shopping. We can take a dog for a walk. There are lots of jobs we can do."

"Yes!" said Lee. "Then I'll have some money for the fair!"

Chapter 2

The three friends went off to
find some jobs to do.

First they went to see Sam's dad.

"We want to make some money,"
said Sam. "Then Lee can come to
the fair with us. Do you have any
jobs we can do?"

"Yes, you can wash my car," said
Sam's dad.

"Great!" said Lee. "I'll soon have some
money for the fair."

Raj, Sam and Lee went to get a
bucket of water and some old rags.
They began to wash the car.
"Your dad's car is very dirty,"
said Lee.
"No, it's not!" said Sam.
And she threw some water at Lee.

The water hit Lee in the face.

"Urgh! I'm all wet!" shouted Lee.

"I'll get you for that!"

Lee threw some water at Sam.

The water hit her in the face.

"Urgh! Now I'm all wet too!"

said Sam.

"I'm not wet!" shouted Raj.
So Sam and Lee threw some
water at him.
"You are now!" said Sam and Lee.
They all laughed.

Sam's dad came out to see what was
going on. He was very cross.
"Look at the mess you've made,"
he shouted. "I will have to wash the
car myself."
"Now we won't get any money,"
said Lee.
"We'll have to look for some more jobs
to do," said Sam.

The friends went to see Raj's mum.
She was having a cup of tea with
Mrs Green. Mrs Green lived across
the street.

"Can we do any jobs for you, Mum?"
asked Raj. "We want to make
some money."
"Then Lee can come to the fair with
us," said Sam
"I'm sorry, but I don't have any
jobs for you," said Raj's mum.

"I have a job for you," said
Mrs Green. "You can take my dog,
Micky, for a walk."
"OK," said Lee. "But I will have to ask
my mum."
"And I will have to ask my dad,"
said Sam.

Lee and Sam went home, and
Mrs Green went to get Micky.
Micky was a little brown dog.
He jumped about and barked a lot.
"Be a good dog, Micky," said
Mrs Green.
"Woof!" barked Micky.

The friends took Micky to the
park at the end of the street.
There was a little girl in the park with
her mum. The little girl was playing
with a ball. Micky ran after the ball
and got hold of it.
"Give the ball back, Micky!" said Raj.

But Micky didn't want to.
"Let go, Micky!" shouted Sam.
But Micky wouldn't.
"I want my ball back!" said the
little girl.

Lee gave Micky a dog biscuit.
Micky let go of the ball and Lee gave
it back to the little girl.
"You're a bad dog, Micky!" said Lee.

Raj, Sam and Lee took Micky back to
Mrs Green.

"Thank you," said Mrs Green.

And she gave Lee a pound.

"Cool!" said Lee. "Now I've got some
money for the fair!"

Just then, the little girl and her
mum came up the street.
The little girl was crying.
"Look what that dog did to my ball!"
she said.
Lee looked at the ball.
It was as flat as a pancake.

"Don't cry," said Lee. "You can get a new ball."

And he gave the little girl the pound.

"Thank you," said the girl.

"Now I haven't got any money for the fair!" said Lee.

Chapter 3

Lee was fed up. He had no money for the fair. He had to find some more jobs to do.

"What jobs can I do now?" he asked his friends.

"My mum hasn't got any jobs for us," said Raj.

"And my dad won't give us any more jobs!" said Sam.

Then they saw a woman walking by.

She had a big bag of heavy shopping.

Something fell out of her bag.

But the woman didn't see.

She walked on up the street.

"Look!" said Lee. "What's that?"

Raj, Sam and Lee went to look.

There was a purse on the ground.

"It must be that woman's purse,"
said Sam.

"That's what fell out of her bag,"
said Lee.

Lee picked up the purse.

"Wow! There's a lot of money in here," he said.

Raj and Sam looked at Lee.

"You could keep it," said Raj.

"Then you could have a really good time at the fair," said Sam.

"Yes, I could," said Lee.

They all looked at the purse.

"I can't keep it," said Lee. "It's
not mine."

"No, you can't keep it," said Sam.

"What shall we do?" asked Raj.

"I'll go and look for her," said Lee.

Lee ran off up the street.

He saw the woman standing at the bus stop.

"You dropped your purse," said Lee. "Here it is."

"Thank you very much," said the woman. "What a good boy you are." And she opened the purse and gave Lee five pounds!

"Thank you very much," said Lee.

Lee ran back to Raj and Sam.

"Guess what?" he said. "The woman gave me five pounds! Now I can go to the fair."

"We can go on the ghost train," said Raj.

"We can go on the big wheel," said Sam.

"And we can eat lots of candy floss," said Lee.

"YES!" said Raj, Sam and Lee.